Jacqueline Wilson

Illustrated by
NICK SHARRATT

ASK
TRACY BEAKER
and Friends

Do you ever wish there were magic answers to all your problems? Do you want to know if you'll ever get a puppy or a kitten? Do you wonder how to deal with your annoying little sister? Do you want to find out if you'll do well in your exams? Well, this special book has ALL the answers. Mind you, I wouldn't always trust Tracy Beaker and her friends to know absolutely everything!

This is a fun way to solve all your little niggling queries. Think of a question, open the book anywhere you like, and see what the advice is on the right-hand page. If you don't like the answer, you can always try all over again.

You can keep a record of your questions on the left-hand page, and write about your daily life, confiding all your secret thoughts. Many of my favourite fictional characters keep journals. This is your chance to write about your life in this special book.

I kept a journal right throughout my childhood. I'd often ask myself questions too. They were often very silly, like *Could I grow long blond hair down to my waist?* When I was a teenager I frequently asked my diary *How will I ever get a proper boyfriend?* But the question I asked over and over again was this one: *Will I get to be a writer when I grow up?* Most of my journal dreams have come true. I hope yours do too!

Jacqueline Wilson

DATE

☆ Tracy says ☆

I DARE YOU TO!

DATE

 Beauty says ☆

YOU'LL FEEL BETTER IF YOU CUDDLE YOUR PET

DATE

☆ Hetty says ☆

IT'S TIME TO GO ON A JOURNEY

DATE

☆ Mr Speed says ☆

TAKE UP A NEW SPORT

DATE

☆ India says ☆

KEEPING A DIARY HELPS YOU SORT OUT YOUR THOUGHTS

DATE

☆ Sadie says ☆

JUST LET IT ALL OUT!

DATE

☆ Violet says ☆

DO SOMETHING CREATIVE

DATE

☆ Ruby says ☆

IT WON'T BE AS EMBARRASSING AS YOU THINK

DATE

☆ Charlie says ☆

TRY MEETING YOUR NEIGHBOURS

DATE

☆ Miranda says ☆

YOU'LL BE BOWLED OVER!

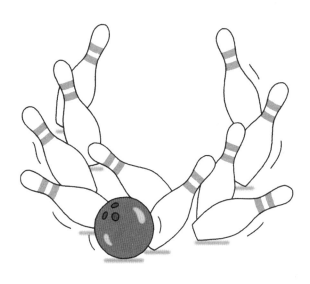

DATE

☆ Tracy says ☆

JUST GO FOR A BURGER!

DATE

 ☆ Gemma says ☆

YOU CAN RELY ON A REALLY GOOD FRIEND

DATE

☆ Em says ☆

CHOOSE A GOOD ROLE MODEL

DATE

☆ Floss says ☆

DON'T LET YOURSELF BE BOSSED AROUND

DATE

☆ Prue says ☆

THERE'S MORE TO LIFE THAN MAKE-UP

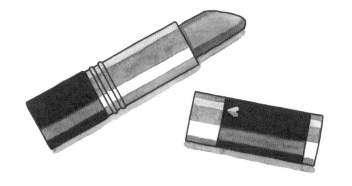

DATE

☆ Tracy says ☆
IT'S TIME TO RELAX

DATE

☆ Mandy says ☆

BE KIND TO SOMEONE YOU LOVE

DATE

☆ Claire says ☆

TRY NOT TO WORRY

DATE

☆ Sylvie says ☆

BE CAREFUL

DATE

☆ Beauty says ☆

DON'T GIVE UP

DATE

☆ Tracy says ☆

DON'T BE SCARED

DATE

☆ Treasure says ☆

NO!

DATE

☆ Ruby and Garnet say ☆

STICK TOGETHER

DATE

☆ Hetty says ☆

BE BRAVE

DATE

☆ Daisy says ☆

REMEMBER WHO YOUR REAL FRIENDS ARE

DATE
_____
_____
_____
_____
_____
_____
_____
_____
_____
_____
_____
_____
_____
_____
_____
_____
_____

☆ Lizzie says ☆

DO SOMETHING FUN

DATE

DATE

☆ Sadie says ☆

MAKE SOMEONE LAUGH

DATE

☆ Lottie says ☆

WORK HARD

DATE

☆ Em says ☆

MAKE THE MOST OF IT

DATE

☆ Elsa says ☆

CHEER EVERYONE UP WITH A JOKE

DATE

☆ Cam says ☆

ENJOY SIMPLE PLEASURES

DATE

☆ Gemma says ☆

APPRECIATE YOUR FAMILY

DATE

☆ Prue says ☆

FOLLOW
YOUR HEART

DATE

☆ Floss says ☆

SHARE YOUR
FAVOURITE STORY

DATE

 ☆ Ellie says ☆

LOVE THE WAY
YOU LOOK

DATE

☆ Miss Simpkins says ☆

COOL IT!

DATE

☆ Beauty says ☆

USE YOUR TALENTS

DATE

☆ Sadie says ☆

TAKE IT IN YOUR STRIDE

DATE

☆ Dolphin says ☆

TRY TO REMEMBER
THE GOOD TIMES

DATE

 ☆ Tracy says ☆

COME UP WITH A NEW IDEA

DATE

☆ Hetty says ☆

HOLD FAST
TO YOUR DREAMS

DATE

☆ Lizzie says ☆

SMILE!

DATE

☆ Mandy says ☆

HONESTY IS THE BEST POLICY

DATE

☆ Daisy says ☆

STICK UP FOR WHAT YOU KNOW IS RIGHT

DATE

☆ Tracy says ☆

BE A STAR!

DATE

☆ Charlie says ☆

TALK TO SOMEONE YOU TRUST

DATE

☆ Sylvie says ☆

PHONE A FRIEND

DATE

☆ Ruby says ☆

AIM HIGH

DATE

☆ Rax says ☆

SET THE WORLD ALIGHT!

DATE

☆ Tracy says ☆

MIX UP SOME MAGIC

DATE

 ☆ Gemma says ☆

MAKE YOUR FEELINGS KNOWN

DATE

☆ Pearl says ☆

MAKE A WISH

DATE

☆ Dixie says ☆

MUCK IN AND HELP

DATE

☆ Sadie says ☆

THINK ABOUT YOUR FUTURE

DATE

☆ Tracy says ☆

I DARE YOU NOT TO!

DATE

☆ Andy says ☆

LOOK FOR FRIENDS IN UNEXPECTED PLACES

DATE

☆ Ruby says ☆

INTREPID EXPLORERS USE NATURAL RESOURCES!

DATE

☆ Gemma and Alice say ☆

ENJOY A GOOD MEAL

DATE

☆ Ellie says ☆

SHOW THEM WHO'S BOSS!

DATE

☆ Tracy says ☆

HAVE A LAUGH!

DATE

☆ Elsa says ☆

BE AS TOUGH AS OLD BOOTS

DATE

☆ Lizzie says ☆

LEND A HAND

DATE

☆ Em says ☆

SHARE THE FUN

DATE

☆ Lottie says ☆

MAKE THE MOST OF NEW EXPERIENCES

DATE

EMBARRASSING MOMENTS DON'T LAST FOR EVER

DATE

☆ Cam says ☆

WRAP UP WARM

DATE

KEEP IN TOUCH
WITH OLD FRIENDS

DATE

☆ Tim says ☆

HANG ON IN THERE!

DATE

☆ Jade says ☆

GO FOR A RUN TO RELAX

DATE

☆ Football says ☆

KEEP WORKING ON YOUR SKILLS

DATE

☆ Holly says ☆

LET SOMEONE ELSE TAKE CARE OF YOU SOMETIMES

DATE

☆ Treasure says ☆

TAKE COMFORT IN A GOOD BOOK

DATE

☆ Lola Rose says ☆

TURN TO SOMEONE YOU CAN TRUST

DATE

☆ Ellie says ☆

LOOKS AREN'T EVERYTHING

DATE

 Tracy says

SOMETIMES YOU CAN HAVE YOUR CAKE AND EAT IT!

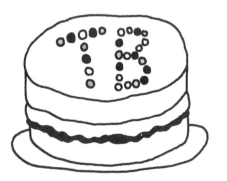

DATE

 ☆ Biscuits says ☆

BE YOUR OWN SUPERHERO!

DATE

☆ Beauty says ☆

YOU'RE NEVER TOO OLD FOR YOUR TEDDY

DATE

☆ Daisy says ☆

DON'T BE TAKEN IN BY APPEARANCES

DATE

☆ India says ☆

REAL FRIENDS ARE
THE BEST

DATE

☆ Verity says ☆

KNOW WHEN
TO SAY GOODBYE

DATE

☆ Tracy says ☆

STAND UP FOR YOURSELF

DATE

☆ Tanya says ☆

REMEMBER HOW LUCKY YOU ARE

DATE

☆ Elsa says ☆

IT'S NOT ALWAYS THE RIGHT TIME FOR A JOKE

DATE

☆ Lizzie says ☆

GIVE NEW PEOPLE A CHANCE

DATE

☆ Cam says ☆

YOU DESERVE
A TREAT

DATE

☆ Gemma says ☆

GET STUCK IN!

DATE

☆ Lola Rose says ☆

FACE YOUR FEARS

DATE

☆ Sadie says ☆

US GIRLS STICK TOGETHER

DATE

☆ Charlie says ☆

SURPRISE YOURSELF!

DATE

☆ Tracy says ☆

HIT THE JACKPOT!

DATE

 William says

EVERYBODY IS GOOD AT SOMETHING

DATE

☆ Biscuits says ☆

ALWAYS TAKE
SUPPLIES!

DATE

☆ Ruby says ☆

GET YOUR OWN BACK!

DATE

☆ Floss says ☆

BE PROUD
OF YOURSELF

DATE

☆ Tracy says ☆

USE YOUR
IMAGINATION

DATE

☆ Gemma says ☆

TRY DOING
SOMETHING NEW

DATE

☆ Ruby says ☆

JUST BE YOURSELF

DATE

☆ Elsa says ☆

YOU CAN BE
A STAR

DATE _____
_____
_____
_____
_____
_____
_____
_____
_____
_____
_____
_____
_____
_____
_____
_____
_____
_____
_____
_____
_____

☆ Tracy says ☆

YOU KNOW WHO
YOU CAN TRUST

HETTY FEATHER

Jacqueline Wilson

ROLL UP, ROLL UP . . .
for the amazing tale of HETTY FEATHER.

GASP as she is abandoned as a baby!
SHUDDER at the hardship she suffers!
WONDER at the search for her real mother!

And enjoy this sensational new bestseller, set in
the reign of Queen Victoria, with a heroine every
bit as feisty as any twenty-first century girl.

'*Hetty Feather* is the most compelling tale
Wilson has told' *The Times*

'Simply the best. Truly brilliant' *Sun*

Doubleday
978 0 385 61444 3

LITTLE DARLINGS

Jacqueline Wilson

Two very different girls — one extraordinary friendship!

Sunset lives a glamorous celebrity lifestyle with
her rock-star dad and model mum — but yearns
for some peace and a real friend.

Destiny is the same age as Sunset but her life couldn't
be more different. She and her mum live on the edge of
a rundown estate, worrying about money and illness.

When the two girls' paths cross, a surprising truth
is revealed and a very special connection is formed . . .

The latest bestseller from a prize-winning author,
one of the most popular writers in Britain for
over a decade.

Doubleday
978 0 385 61443 6

ALSO AVAILABLE BY JACQUELINE WILSON

JOIN THE **FREE** ONLINE

☆ FAN CLUB ☆

Read Jacqueline's monthly diary, look up tour info, receive fan club e-newsletters.

All this and more, including a fab message board, members' jokes and loads of exclusive top offers.

 Visit **www.jacquelinewilson.co.uk**
for more info!

ASK TRACY BEAKER AND FRIENDS
A DOUBLEDAY BOOK 978 0 385 61880 9

Published in Great Britain by Doubleday,
an imprint of Random House Children's Books
A Random House Group company

This edition published 2010

1 3 5 7 9 10 8 6 4 2

Text copyright © Jacqueline Wilson, 2010
Illustrations copyright © Nick Sharratt, 2010

The right of Jacqueline Wilson to be identified as the author
of this work has been asserted in accordance with the
Copyright, Designs and Patents Act 1988.

Compiled by Alexandra Antscherl

The Random House Group Limited supports the Forest Stewardship
Council (FSC), the leading international forest certification organization.
All our titles that are printed on Greenpeace-approved FSC-certified paper
carry the FSC logo. Our paper procurement policy can be found at
www.rbooks.co.uk/environment.

RANDOM HOUSE CHILDREN'S BOOKS
61–63 Uxbridge Road, London W5 5SA

www.kidsatrandomhouse.co.uk
www.rbooks.co.uk

Addresses for companies within The Random House Group Limited
can be found at: www.randomhouse.co.uk/offices.htm

THE RANDOM HOUSE GROUP Limited Reg. No. 954009

A CIP catalogue record for this book is available
from the British Library.

Printed and bound in China